AMAZING MAZES

Mind Bending Mazes

for Ages 6-60

BARNES
&NOBLE
BOOKS
NEW YORK

Rolf Heimann

First published as *Amazing Mazes*. *Amazing Mazes 2*. *Amazing Mazes 3*
by Roland Harvey Books in Australia in 1989, 1994, 1996

This edition first published in 2001 by Barnes & Noble
122 Fifth Avenue
New York
NY 10011

Publishing agreement arranged by the Australian Licensing Corporation

Printed in China
Library of Congress Cataloguing in Publication Data

Heimann, Rolf, 1940-

Amazing mazes collection

ISBN 0 7607 2180 7

1. Maze puzzles - Juvenile Literature. 1. Title.

793.73

Amazing History

The world's most famous maze is without a doubt the 'labyrinth' of ancient Minoan mythology. It was built by Daedalus to imprison the 'Minotaur', a man-eating monster. Whoever entered the labyrinth could abandon all hope of ever finding the way out. People were forced into its dark passages to be devoured by the Minotaur as human sacrifices.

The Athenian prince, Theseus, finally volunteered to be sacrificed, secretly planning to slay the monster. He succeeded in doing so and even found his way out with the aid of a long thread given to him by Ariadne, the king's daughter who had fallen in love with Theseus.

The story is, of course, a legend. But archaeologists were surprised when they excavated the ruins of Minoan palaces in the island of Crete. The intricate layouts of these palaces – some with as many as 1500 rooms – reminded them of mazes.

Many civilisations throughout the ages used mazes, usually for amusement. Even today we have fair-grounds that feature mirror mazes and people pay good money for the fun of getting lost! Modern scientists use mazes as part of intelligence tests for animals, as well as for people.

Hundreds of years ago, architects often incorporated maze designs in the decoration of churches and other buildings. They looked upon these designs, with their confusing paths and many dead-ends, as symbols of our journey through life. How often we are in doubt about which path to take! Sometimes it is only a lucky guess that puts us on the right track. But even if we meet one dead-end after another we must not get disheartened.

Lila, Tom and Ben are confronted by all sorts of mazes in this book. Some are very easy and some are quite difficult. Lila is the oldest and will attempt the hardest ones. Ben, the youngest, will do the easier ones while Tom goes for those in between.

My name – "CONNY" – is somehow hidden on every page of this book. There it is, in the corner!

1 The Labyrinth

Lila, Tom and Ben are visiting a film studio – and what a thrill it is! Tom recognises the famous film star Miss Lemour and asks for her autograph.

'Sure honey,' she says, 'but be a darling and plug in my hair dryer. It must be one of those cables over there …'

Miss Lemour hasn't even noticed that her poodle, Fifi, has wandered off onto the film set. Ben discovers Fifi but can't reach her, even when he stands on the sign. Will the dog be able to get back to where the ladder leans against the wall?

In the meantime Lila hears distressed calls from two workmen who have been putting finishing touches to the Minotaur's Maze. Now they can't find their way out!

From the top of the ladder Lila should be able to guide them back.

Solution on page 29

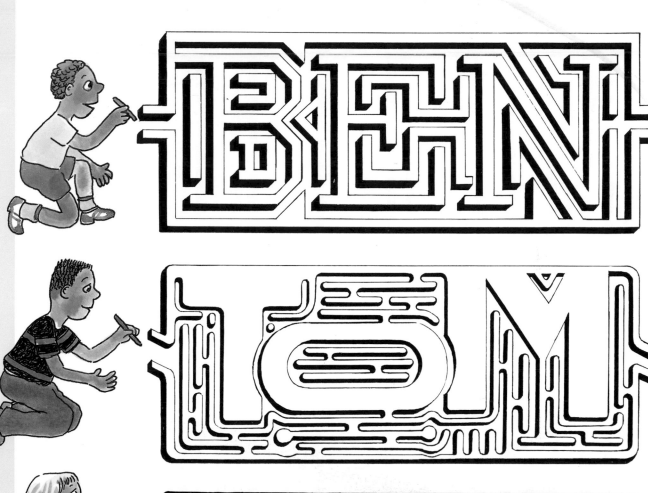

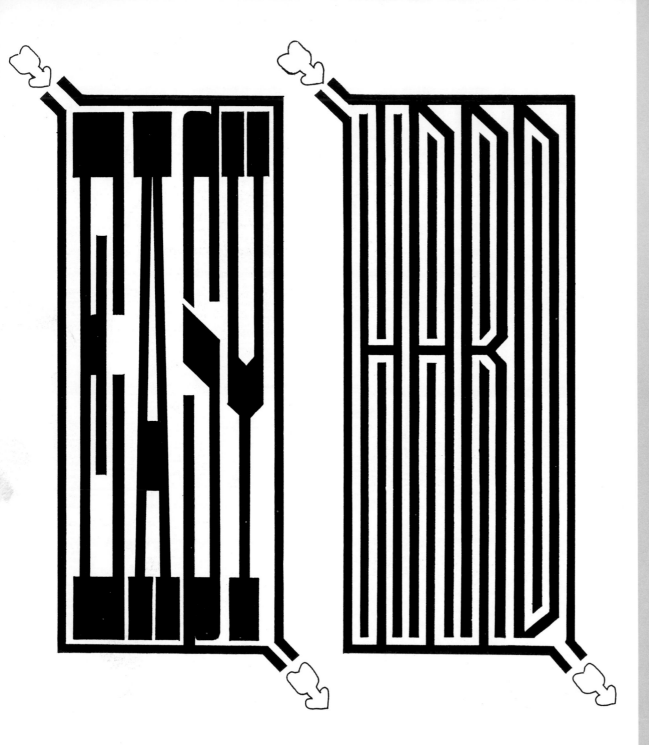

2 Drinks in the Pipeline

Lila, Tom and Ben are thirsty. There are three glasses near the lower tanks. But what sort of juice do these tanks hold? The children will have to work it out by following the pipes. Ben likes orange juice, Tom wants lime and Lila feels like some lemonade.

Solution on page 29

Here's a hint, Lila: when you come to a junction, go with the even numbers...

I wonder if I can get that bird seed without stepping over any black lines?

Professor McQueen is an inventor who wants to make housework easier. At the moment he is tinkering with a machine that pours the tea and adds milk and sugar. He is very proud of his invention.

But maybe he got a bit carried away this time. He can't even remember which lever operated what and whether he was to push or to pull. In desperation he asks Lila to check his patented sugar dispenser, Tom has to work out how the milk is added and Ben must check the tea-pouring mechanism.

Solution on page 29

Conny wants him to invent a birdseed dispenser.

4   Matching Socks

Now that they have finished the washing, Ben, Tom and Lila have to find their way to the clothesline so that they can match up their socks. Start on the white platform where the odd socks are lying.

Solution on page 29

Solution on page 28

Solution on page 28

5 Puzzling Picnic

Ben, Tom and Lila have climbed the lookout tower to check the park's layout before setting out to buy a few more things for their picnic on the lawn.

Ben decides to take the blue boat to buy some apples while Tom will take the other boat to the lemonade stand. In the meantime, Lila will go by foot to the ice-cream parlour.

Solution on page 30

Want some help in making sense of the signposts? The tip is "codeword icecream"

Step only on the panels that contain objects that begin with A. For example: apple, arrow . . .

And if you get stuck, *some* of these words might help: atom, aardvark, atoll, avocado, Australia, armour, asp, ankle, antlers, awning and antique.

Solution on page 28

Solution on page 28

6 The Coolangatoo

The good old *Coolangatoo* is not the most efficient ship. In fact Captain Crabweed needs all the help he can get to run it. When his cap falls onto the foredeck he asks Ben to bring it up to him. Ben has quite a job finding his way up to the bridge.

Then the Captain wants to give three short blasts on the whistle, but the rope has broken! He sends Tom into the engine room to operate the whistle from there. Can you help Tom find the right pipe?

Lila has the hard job. She will have to untangle the telephone lines that connect the bridge to the ship below. They are in a real mess! Start with the engine room line.

Solution on page 30

16

7 Go Fly a Kite

Flying kites is a lot of fun, but not when they get stuck in a tree like this!

'Stay where you are!' cries the owner of the garden. 'I don't want you to damage my precious Himalayan Spine Tree. Just tell me which kite is yours and I'll get it for you.'

Can you work out the owner of each kite?

Solution on page 30

Imagine building a nest among those spines!

A quiet Sunday stroll to the park . . .

17

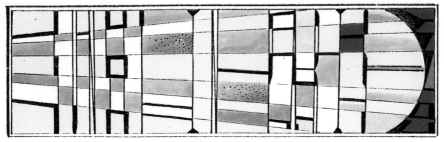

8 Challenging Chambers

At first glance this job really looks hard. The children have to take the pegs from the centre tower and fit them through the holes in the chambers until they reach the bottom.

But Lila soon finds that it's not as difficult as it looks. The objects in the chambers are a good guide.

Lila takes the round peg through the chambers that have an object starting with C – 'C' for 'circular'.

Tom discovers that the star-shaped peg goes through the chambers that have objects starting with S.

'I can't spell!' cries Ben. But that doesn't matter. He can still recognise the diamond-shaped holes through which to push his peg.

Solution on page 30

Solution on page 30

18

9 Lasseter's Reef

Lasseter's gold reef has been rediscovered!

But it's not so easy to get there through the maze of mine shafts and tunnels. Lila, Tom and Ben have each staked a claim.

Solution on page 31

Don't forget, my name - Conny - appears on every page!

Dazzling Duet

Here are two mazes. See if you can find your way through both in under 90 seconds.

10 Log Jam

Ben will take the red canoe and find a path through the floating logs to Middle Island, where Uncle Alf is chopping down the last three trees.

Tom will take the blue canoe and bring some dry socks to Uncle Joe.

There is no canoe left for Lila. She will have to walk over the logs to Rocky Island to tell the men they're wanted on the telephone.

Solution on page 31

Make your way down by stepping only on the objects that are made of wood.

Solution on page 28

23

11 Tracks in the Snow

It is winter and the snow is full of tracks.

'Look!' cries Ben. 'A rabbit went past here. Let's follow the paw prints and find out where it went!'

'Never mind the rabbit,' says Tom. 'Somebody took the nose from our snowman. And the rascal's footprints are still in the snow – let's follow them and find out who he is!'

'I don't want to waste my time on that,' says Lila. 'I'm following these ski tracks here. They're from my friend Elisa and I want to find out where she went.'

Solution on page 31

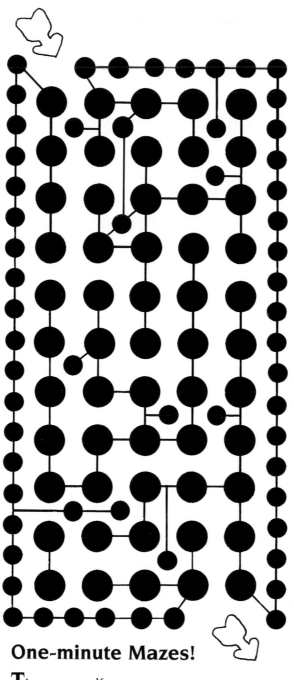

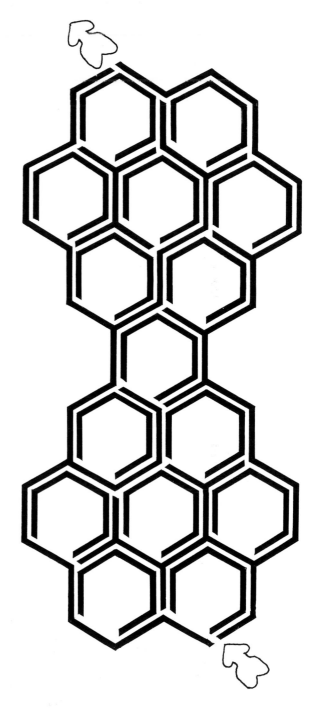

One-minute Mazes!

Time yourself
– under one minute per maze: marvellous
– under two minutes: moderate
– over two minutes: miserable!

25

Step from A to Z through the entire alphabet. For example, start on A, then move to the Book for B, then to the Cup for C, and so on.
Solution on page 28

12 Fruitful Quest

Lila wants to pick some cherries, Tom will get the plums and Ben the lemons. They should have a lot of fun finding their way to the fruit trees.

Ben will be guided by the sign of the lemons. Tom, if he keeps his eyes open, will find the whole alphabet on the way. Lila has the longest path, but if she's smart enough she will discover an encouraging message as she goes.

Solution on page 31

Did you know that even blind people can find their way through a maze if they stick to a simple rule? If your left hand always stays in touch with the left wall (or your right hand with the right wall) you can be sure to end up at the exit. It may take a long time but at least you can't get lost forever. Try it!

Solutions

On the next three pages you will find the solutions to the twelve main mazes. Below are the solutions to the more difficult puzzles and mazes from the other pages.

Page 11: Cockatoo, owl, lark, kookaburra, albatross, sandpiper, robin. The codeword on the lower picture is SUNLIGHT.

Page 13: Apple, arrow, armour, avocado, Africa, ant, asparagus, atom, armchair, alarm-clock, animal, anchor, archway, atoll, aeroplane, arm, arrow, antlers, awning, astronaut, acorn, apple, arrow, Australia, atom, apple.

Page 14

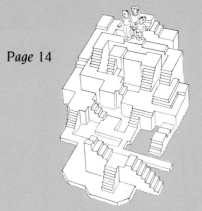

Page 23: Cradle, tree stump, chair, chest, log, table, tree, bowl, fence, gate.

Page 26: A, book, cup, drum, eye, flower, glasses, house, island, jar, kangaroo, leaf, matches, nose, octopus, pan, Queen, rope, scissors, television, unicorn, violin, water, xylophone, yellow, Z.

1 The Labyrinth

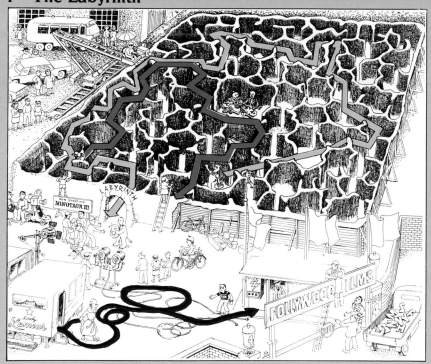

2 Drinks in the Pipeline

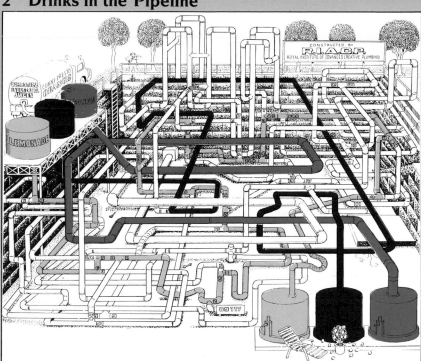

3 Professor McQueen's Breakfast Machine

4 Matching Socks

5 Puzzling Picnic

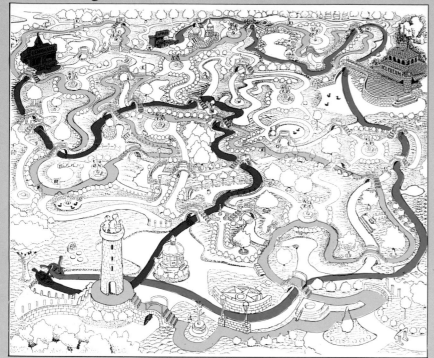

6 The Coolangatoo

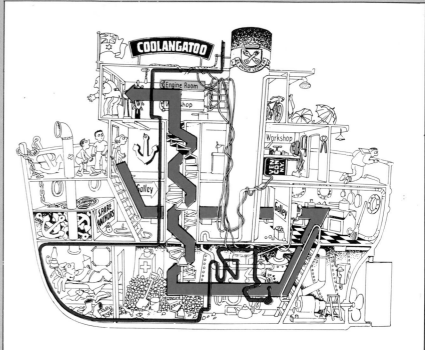

7 Go Fly a Kite

8 Challenging Chambers

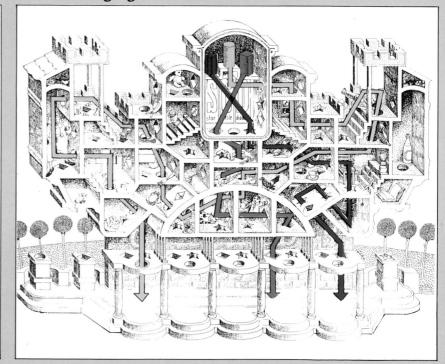

9 Lasseter's Reef

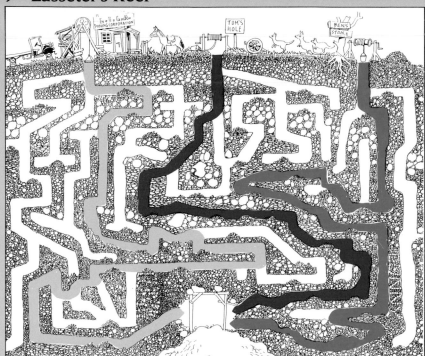

10 Log Jam

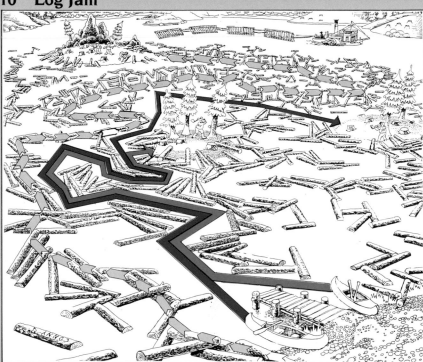

11 Tracks in the Snow

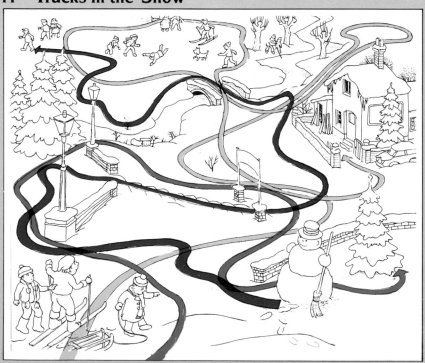

12 Fruitful Quest

Lila's encouraging message was:
You are doing well! Congratulations

And here's one for the road !

Rolf Heimann's
AMAZING MAZES

Amazing History

This maze on the right can be found on the floor of the cathedral of Chartres in France. Years ago, pilgrims who could not afford the time and money to travel to Jerusalem made their way through the maze on their knees. This was a kind of substitute trip to the Holy Land. When pilgrims could afford to go there by plane, the maze was no longer used, except by children who amused themselves during long church services! These days the maze is usually covered by rows of chairs, so that children will no longer interrupt the church services with their laughter.

Mazes are irresistible to many people, not only when they are bored. Since you are no longer able to walk your way through the Chartres maze, I have redrawn it for you here. So, pilgrim, progress through it and the rest of the book, with my best wishes for a safe and successful journey.

My name appears on every page of this book. It's "CONNY". Apart from the CONNY in this corner it appears 5 more times on this page. Solutions start on page 28.

3

"This maze looks much too difficult for me," said Ben. "Maybe it is," agreed Lila, "so here is a hint for you: turn right 8 times. After that you're on your own. Tom, you go with him. When you reach the top, it's you who has to lead the way back - but not the same way! You have to come back through the other half. And let me tell you - the two halves are not quite the same."
"What are you going to do?" Ben asked Lila.
"I'm going to put up that ladder and search for the three spots which make the left half different from the right half."

Ben will always take the easiest maze, Lila the hardest and Tom the one in between.

Only one of the entrances leads to the tower. Can you find it ?

2 Snail trails

There's been a disaster at the International Snail Research Centre! Who would have believed that the snails would be strong enough to break out? There were 3 kinds: the Californian Pink Foot, the Tasmanian Wriggle-tail and the Nanasato Green. Luckily they left their trails behind so that they can be traced. This is the children's job. Lila will try to collect all the Wriggle-tails, Tom the Pinkfoots and Ben the Nanasato Greens.

If those snails keep escaping, I recommend snail insurance!

3 Frozen footpaths

"I think the ice is breaking up," said Lila. "We had better get back to the boat. Ben, take the shortest route back, and Tom, you collect our picnic basket. I'm going back ashore to close the door of the Nissen hut. Someone forgot to close it. I'll meet you back on the ship!"

This game is called one-upmanship. Find your way from top to bottom by picking things that are one-up on the next. It is possible that there is more than one way through!

Solution on page 28

9

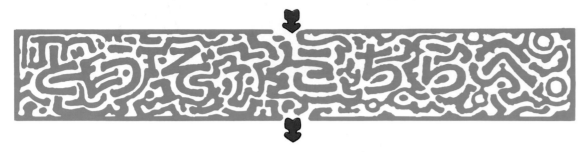

Time limit : 30 seconds.

Time limit : 20 seconds.

Time limit : 30 seconds.

Time limit : 20 seconds.

Calamitous contraption

Will it work? That depends not only on the specially bred Madagascan Malstock Beast, but on how well the children can operate the contraption. Ben will apply the brakes, but will he have to pull the lever up or down? And which way does Tom turn the wheel to lower the carrot? It is Lila's job to find out whether the vehicle will move backwards or forwards once it is in motion.

I wish they would add a propeller!

5 | Coconut confusion

Ben, Tom and Lila went to visit their friends in Samoa. Lila will help guide Uncle Tufia's canoe through the coral reefs so that he can deliver his fresh coconuts to the ship. Tom wants to come along too.

"I'm afraid not," said Uncle Tufia. "The boat is already overloaded, but we will give you a lift on the way back. Make your way to the beacon-island, right near the ship and wait for us there."

Meanwhile Ben was fishing with his friends Elisa and Josefa. Can you help Ben work out who has caught the fish?

I hope they checked the tides...

Stepping stones

Make your way from top to bottom by following these rules:

 Scissors can cut paper

 Paper can wrap stone

 Stone can blunt scissors

 Water can extinguish fire

 Fire can burn paper

13

I'm not so sure about that. Try it anyway. I'll wait here and watch.

"I read somewhere that you'll find your way out of any maze by keeping your hand on the wall and walking until you find the exit," said Tom.
"Lets try it. I'll go along the right-hand wall and Ben, you go along the left-hand one. Let's see who'll be out first!"
"That's not fair," said Ben.
"The inside wall is shorter, so you'll be out first!"

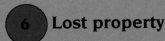

"I don't know why," said Tom, "but this place gives me the creeps. I'm glad we're out of it."
"Bad news," laughed Lila. "You have to go back because I think you left your cap in there!"
Tom touched his head. "You're right! And it's my favourite red one. But what about you, Lila? It looks like you forgot your white socks. And Ben, haven't you lost one of your shoes? Come on, let's all go back and find the way to our lost property."

Wait for me! I'll have to look for my name!

If it's true that the letters "CONNY" are hidden on every page...

14

15

Ben has built some mazes for his pet rat, but he has made a mistake with one of them: it has no way out at all. He has decided to destroy the maze so that none of his pets are driven to madness. Lila is ready to blow it up, and is waiting for Tom to hoist the flag showing the colour of the faulty maze. Let's hope none of them make a mistake!

Colourful connection

Find the odd one out! If you are having trouble, the title of this puzzle might give you a clue. Or is it a red herring?

Solution on page 28

Don't you see it's all a mistake!

These kids have watched too much TV!

Time limit : 30 seconds.

Time limit : 20 seconds.

What is it that these images have in common?

Solution on page 28

Save the beetle !
Time limit: 20 seconds.

This waterslide into the hot springs looks like fun! Ben wants to splash into the hot pool, Tom likes the hotter one and Lila would like to try the hottest. Now all they have to do is find their way through the right entrance and up to the correct starting platform.

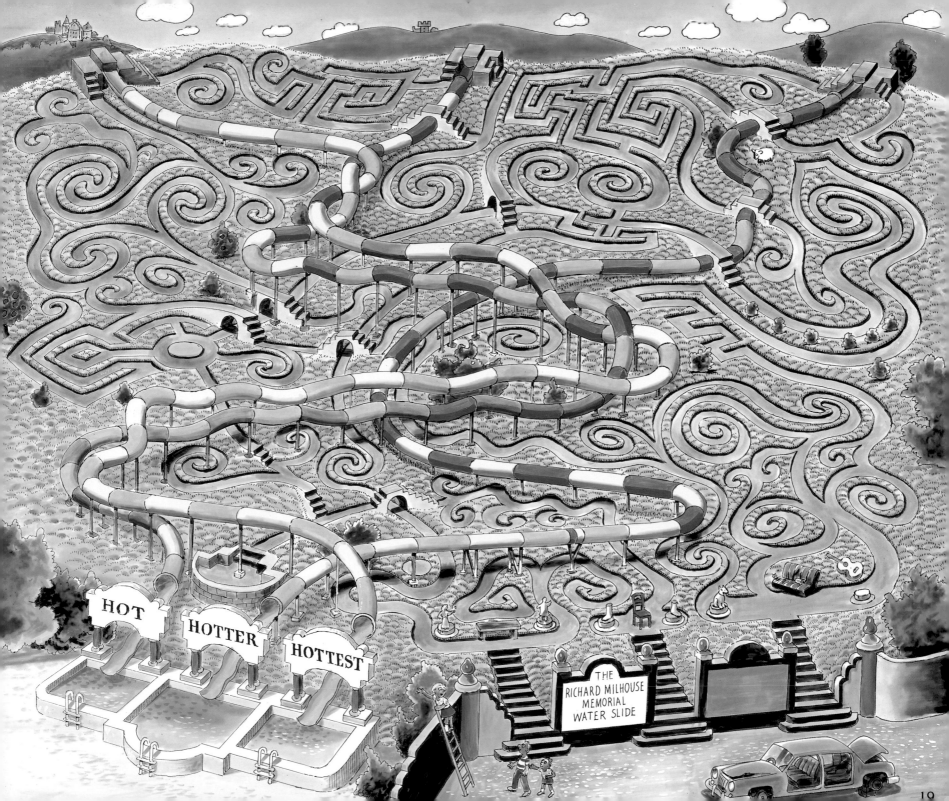

HOT

HOTTER

HOTTEST

THE
RICHARD MILHOUSE
MEMORIAL
WATER SLIDE

19

20

9 Match and swirl

"I like the look of that maze, but where do we have to go?" asked Tom.
"I think we'll know when we find our matching objects!" said Lila.
"Let's go!"

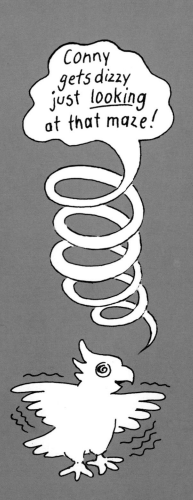

Conny gets dizzy just looking at that maze!

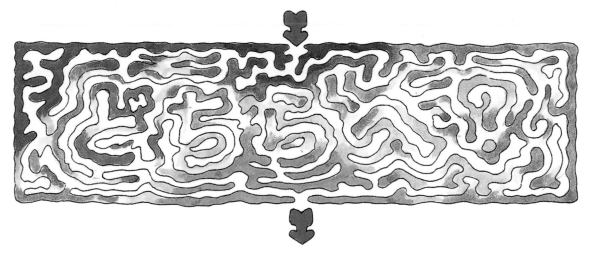

Time limit : 20 seconds.

Make your way to the centre in less than 30 seconds!

**Time limit : 20 seconds.
Good luck!**

You should be able to escape from the centre in all four directions. By the way, the picture is not up the right way. To help you find north, south, east and west, here are the Japanese symbols for each compass point which can be matched to the shapes in the maze:

North   South   East   West

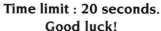

北　南　東　西

Barrel boggle
Which barrel will fill with water?

Ben, Tom and Lila want to eat at their favourite restaurant in Bali, the famous Bamboo Palace. However, after the bridge was destroyed in a flood, it's not so easy to find the way. Lila will walk using any path, Tom will go by bicycle, which means that he can use any path except the ones with steps. Ben has decided to go by taxi, and he will show the driver which way to go. Let's hope there are no roadworks blocking the way!

Burung kakaktua hinggap di jendela...

One day I'll find out what they're singing about...

23

11 Parcelled problems

Lila, Tom and Ben have to make some urgent deliveries. Because the narrow lanes are so hard to get through, they find it easier to find a way over the rooftops. Can you help them to find the best way to deliver their parcels to the right owner?

Time limit : 30 seconds.

Vexing vine

Three minstrels have come to serenade the beautiful princess. Unfortunately they did not know about the fast-growing lawyer-vine. As dawn arrives they find themselves shackled by the vine's tentacles. The only way to save the minstrels is to chop each plant off at the stem. Ben will save the bongo-drummer, Tom will save the alphorn player and Lila will save the lutist.

One-upmanship - page 9

The table has more legs than
Conny, but white ants can eat the
table, the ant-eater can eat the
ants, a centipede has more legs
than an ant-eater, but the snake is
longer, the elephant is heavier,
but the aeroplane can fly, the ship
can carry more passengers, but the
sailing ship does not need fuel,
the house cannot sink, but the
skyscraper has more windows, the
moon is higher, but the
hippopotamus has more letters in
its name! The parrot, though, is
more colourful, the fish can lay
more eggs, but the light-bulb is
much brighter, but the hammer
can smash the light-bulb, the
chest of drawers has more
handles, the fire can burn the
chest, but the rain can extinguish
the fire. The umbrella can keep
rain off, a duck doesn't need an
umbrella, but a cockatoo can
speak better than a duck! Try to
find a different way, and don't be
afraid to be silly: it's silly anyway
to try to be one-up on others!

Colourful connection - page 17

The hat is the odd one out. It is
the only item that does not
contain the colour red.

Solution to puzzle on page 18

The images have the number 2
in common. Two eyes, two wheels,
two birds etc.

1 Half and half

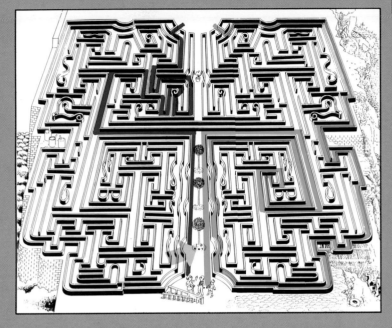

2 Snail trails

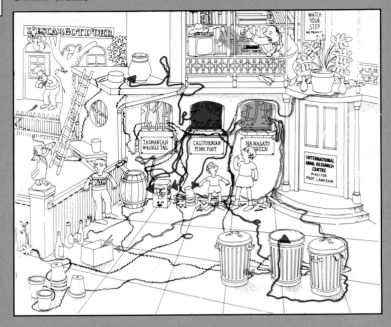

3 Frozen footpath

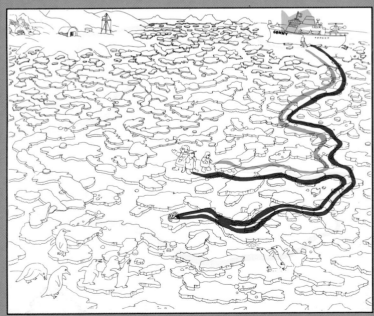

4 Calamitous contraption

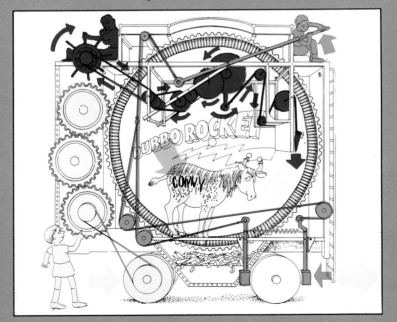

Yellow - Lila   Pink - Tom   Blue - Ben

Green arrow - Conny's name

29

5 Coconut confusion

6 Lost property

7 Ben's blunder

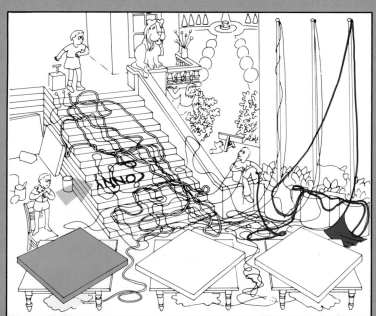

8 Tangled tubes

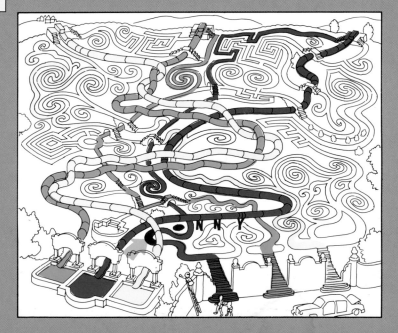

9 Match and swirl

10 Chow chase

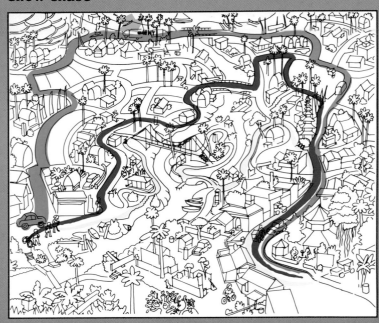

11 Parcelled problems

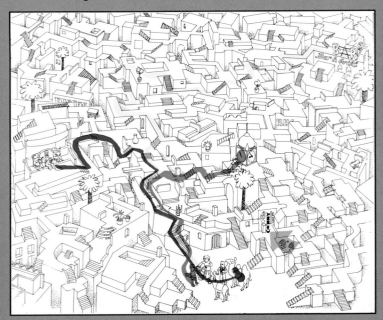

12 Vexing vine

"Let's do an amazing experiment," suggested Tom. "Both of us will keep our hands on the left-hand side wall and walk at the same speed until we come out again. When we meet each other, we'll call out and Lila will know we're exactly halfway through."

"Hmm, we'll see," said Lila. "Ready, set, go!"

Rolf Heimann's
AMAZING MAZES
3

Introduction

Everybody knows the experience of getting lost.
And everybody knows the pleasure and relief of finding the right path again.
To err is human. Nobody goes through life without ever making a mistake. Taking a wrong path may result in being a few minutes late, or it may even lead to disaster. In this book, Rolf Heimann's third in the 'Amazing' series of maze books, any paths taken will lead to nothing but enjoyment. Sometimes there is only one right path, sometimes there are several that lead to the goal. Explore them all! Rush through the following pages or take your time, but above all, **don't give up!**

Hi, I'm Conny! My name is hidden on every page of this book, even on this one. Can you see it?

1 Mouldy Maze

'Hey, what's with all the toadstools?' asked Tom.

Lila explained, 'This is a very dangerous place. These toadstools were grown by the illustrator himself so that we'll fall on something soft if we should slip. He tried mattresses, but they were rather unsightly. Our task is to make a journey and come back to this very spot here without retracing our steps.'

'Sounds easy,' said Tom.

Lila wasn't so sure. Ben had to make his journey without stepping either up or down, Tom had to go down only, and Lila had to find a path stepping up only. Usually such a thing would have been impossible, but this place was built by a fan of Escher.

Who is Escher anyway?

Ben is the youngest. He does the easiest mazes.

Tom is a little older, so his mazes are harder.

Lila, being the oldest of the three, does the hardest mazes of all.

5

Collector's item
A major mistake has been
made in one of these stamps!
Answer on page 28

'Why do I have the feeling we're
being watched?' asked Ben. 'It's
downright scary.'
'You're right,' agreed Tom. 'But you
know, once you find out just what it
is that makes you scared, half your
fear is already gone. Let's find all
those hidden faces and stare right
back at them!'
'Good idea,' agreed Lila, 'but first
we must do what we've been sent
to do. Exchange these three flags
with the old ones of the same colour
that have become a bit tattered.'

Hippy group photo 1975
Peachblossom was, as usual,
between Rain and Starlight.
Tango was then proudly sporting
an Afro hairstyle. Jimini was
wearing his oversized Army
pants. Sunbeam, never without
his hat, was behind Rain and
Lightfoot. What was the name
of the guitar player?
Answer on page 28

6

OH STAIRS
SUBLIME STAIRS
EACH STEP
CLOSER TO THEE.
Johann Wolfgang
von Shakespeare

3 **Domination**

'Correct me if I'm wrong,' said Ben, 'but isn't there only one way to find a path over dominoes, and that is to have dominoes whose ends contain the same number of dots joined up together.'

'Yes, that's the usual way,' agreed Lila, 'and you may use it to make your way to our teddy bear. But there are two other ways as well and they are a bit more difficult. Tom, you must step over the dominoes that are joined together and are the same colour, and I have to step over the dominoes where the colours of the dots match. I'll see you at Teddy Bear Island!'

Would you believe there are 22 differences between the two Egyptian panels above?

Answer on page 28

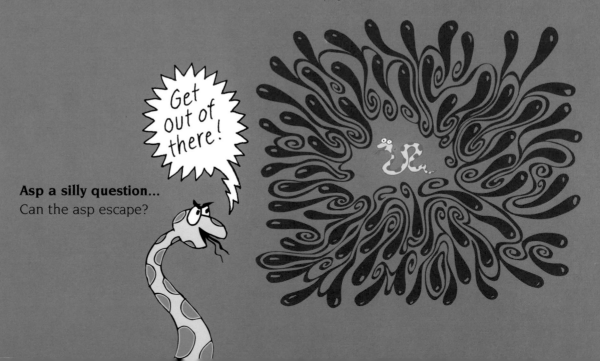

Asp a silly question...
Can the asp escape?

General confusion
Which of the four uniforms matches that worn by General Sloan-Deppenkirk?
Answer on page 28

Mini-mazes:
You should be able to whizz through these in 30 seconds flat!

'Ah, blue and yellow!' exclaimed Tom, 'my favourite colours!'
'Too bad,' said Lila. 'Our job is to paint the tower red. Ben, you find the paint and Tom, you find a brush. Then both of you have to get up the stairs, any stairs, while I stay on the ground and make my way to the door of the tower. I'll meet you at the tower, okay?'

I hate to say it, but it seems an awful waste of time to build such huge mazes!

5 Problem Pets

The children have been told to feed the animals: Tom has a carrot for the rabbit, Lila has a bone for the dog and Ben has some milk for the cat. Won't they get a surprise when they see the size of the animals!

YOU know there's a controversy about whether milk is actually good for cats...

JUST GIMME!

Detective Smart has been given these two surveillance photos. Although he has not been told which of the photos was taken earlier than the other, he knows straight away which one it was.
Answer on page 28

Star Express
Time limit: one minute

13

Early bird gets the worm
Can you get the worm in less than one minute?

6 **Curly Christmas**

'Of all the weird places we've been in, this has to be the weirdest,' exclaimed Tom. 'What do we have to do here?'
'It's simple really,' explained Lila. 'We have to meet at the Christmas tree. Don't get dizzy on the way! Oh! And Merry Christmas!'

I'm going to sell a birdseye view of this maze to the highest bidder!

TOP SECRET

TOP SECRET

GO AWAY!
THERE ARE NO ALIENS*

*It's just swamp gas
or a weather balloon

TAPU

SECRETO

GEHEIM

SEGREDO

立入禁止

RAHASIA

RAHASYAM

ПРЯТАТЬ

GEHEEM · GO HOME

FAA SAINA · ALU ESE

TABOO

7 Alien Assignment

Lila, Tom and Ben have made friends with an alien called Xotltoxox who came in search of his brother, Iboki. Iboki had been captured by the US Air Force and kept in a secret facility near Los Pinos Coladas in New Mexico. 'How are we going to get past the guards?' asked a worried Lila. 'Easy,' said Xotltoxox. 'I know a secret spell that turns military guards into harmless ropossums for five minutes. Ropossums are native animals of my home planet, by the way. But five minutes is all we would have. While I watch the ropossums, you, Ben, find our six-legged space dog, Stripo. And Tom, you find the spacecraft, it looks exactly like mine. And Lila, could you look for my identical twin brother? 'Oh, please, please, please,' begged Ben, 'please, please, please, please tell us that secret spell. It would be worth its weight in gold.' 'I can't do that,' said Xotltoxox. 'A secret is a secret is a secret.'

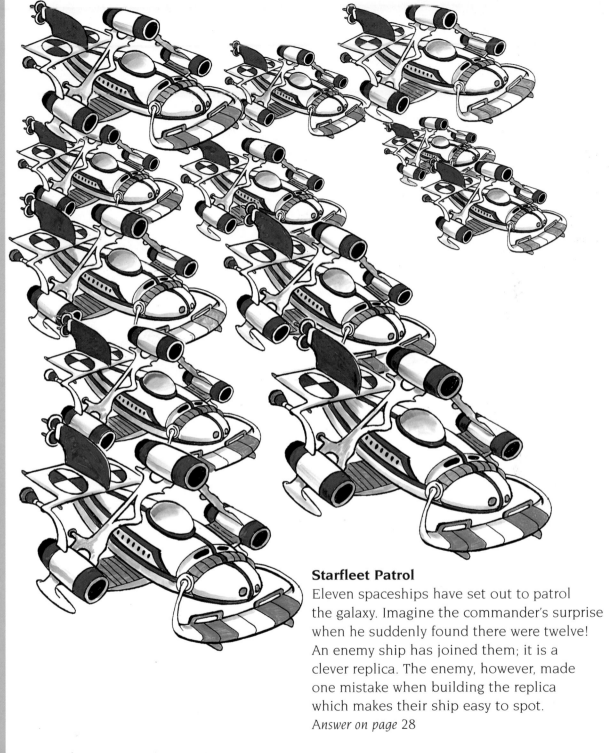

Starfleet Patrol

Eleven spaceships have set out to patrol the galaxy. Imagine the commander's surprise when he suddenly found there were twelve! An enemy ship has joined them; it is a clever replica. The enemy, however, made one mistake when building the replica which makes their ship easy to spot.

Answer on page 28

Surrounded by flowers
Sooner or later our bee has to get back to her hive.
Will she find her way out?

8 Chamber Chase

Lila, Tom and Ben are not the first to enter the tomb of Queen Ysraphel. Grave robbers have been there before and carried away all the gold and silver. But the children have obtained some secret information about the diaries of the ancient Queen. There are three diaries: one from Ysraphel's childhood, one from her teenage years and one from the time when she reigned as a powerful monarch. Because she had been extremely beautiful as well, newspapers and magazines around the world would pay a fortune for those diaries! It is not easy, though, to wade one's way through the maze of underground tunnels and chambers and find the chests that match the sacred symbols obtained by the children.

They look scared. Maybe they want their Mummy!

VORSICHTIG! ОСТОРОЖНЫЙ!
注意深い
CUIDADOSO
CAREFUL!! NATT! NATT!
FÖRSIKTIG
FAAETEETE

9 Rubbish Retrieval

'Isn't it terrible what people still throw away,' said Lila. 'You'd think they'd never heard of recycling or composting.'

'Well, I must admit I recently threw away a red coathanger just because I didn't like its colour,' confessed Tom.

'Shame on you!' exclaimed Lila. 'Go and find it again! And Ben, have you recently thrown away something as well? Something you shouldn't have?'

'Well, I did throw a boomerang ...' Ben admitted sheepishly.

'Didn't it come back? Did you follow the instructions?'

'They were in a foreign language.'

'Oh, I see,' Lila replied. 'Well, get those things back while I dash across the rubbish tip to retrieve my rucksack. But you must stay on the wooden boards. These rubbish tips can be treacherous.'

A boomerang should be the easiest thing to recycle!

My tail is 3 times longer than that of my cat. If it were 10cm longer, it would be twice the size of yours. And if my cat's tail were 10cm shorter, it would be half yours...

Telling tails
Can you work out the length of each creature's tail?

Horseshoe shuffle
Kalamari has passed Foxtrotter and is in the lead while Wild Beauty has slipped to the rear. Hurricane is now positioned between Midnight and Foxtrotter. Which horse is second last?

Answers on page 28

21

The Giant Malayan Butterflower (*Floribustus incredibus*)
The nectar is sweetest right at the centre of the flower,
so help the butterflies find their way to it.

Only two of these jugs are
identical. Which two are they?
Answer on page 28

10 Bothersome Berries

This task may not seem all that difficult, but it's extremely important to get it right.

The problem is that these three different fruits look so much alike that they are easily mistaken for one another. Ben must find the Giant Blue Wobble Cherry (or *Dulcinosa*) which is excellent for use in Blue Forest cake. Then there is the Big Kibble Berry, an excellent natural remedy for toothache. It's botanical name is *Gloriosis*. Tom must identify that.

And finally there is the extremely dangerous Blue Devil's Apple (*Obnoxia fatalis*), so poisonous that Lila must remove it before anyone comes to harm.

Imagine what could happen if there was a mix up!

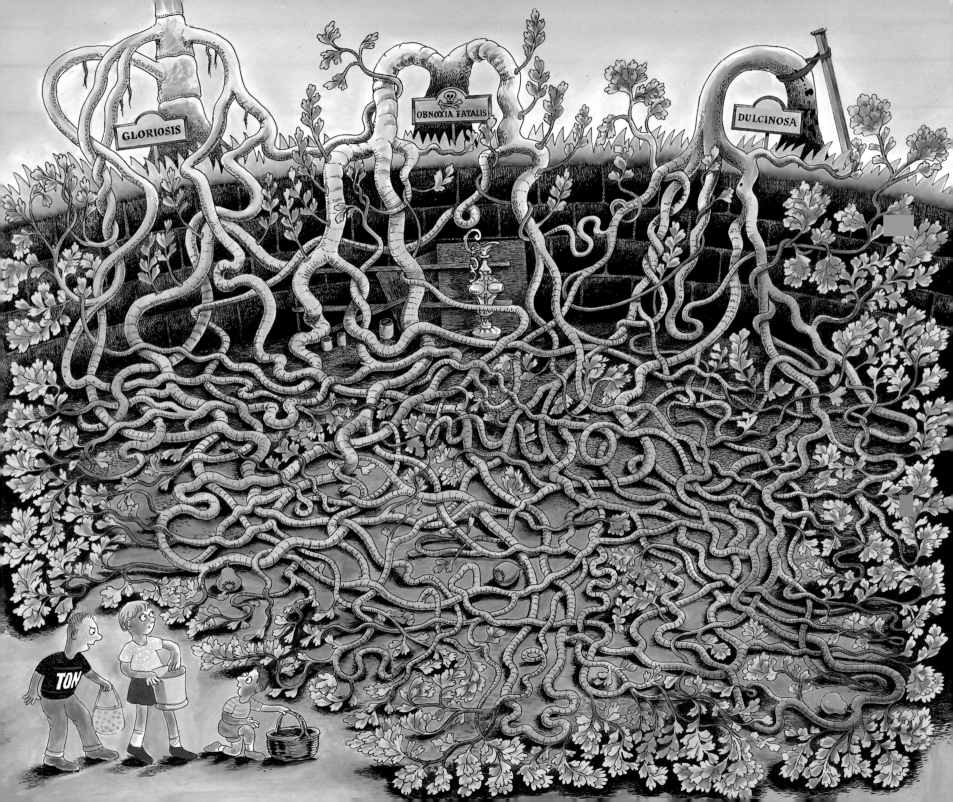

KRONO PARK

CARL NEANDER THAL

T.V. SNACKS

P.C.

ARMSTRONG & ALDRIN
ORVILLE & W. B. U. WRIGHT
THOMAS EDISON
S.F.B. MORSE
W.K. ROENTGEN
KARL-FRIEDRICH BENZ
GUTENBERG
MONTGOLFIER
A.G. BELL
J. LOGIE BAIRD
1957
1896
1932
1969

11 Timeout

'This place is called Kronopark because we have to find our way in chronological order,' explained Lila. 'Chronological order? I hope it isn't painful,' said Ben sounding a little concerned.

Lila laughed. '*Chronological* means arranged in the correct order according to the time in which something happened. Ben, you guide us on the right path, while Tom puts these names to the monuments they belong to. I'll put these signs with the year on the right spot. It'll be like a walk through history.'

'Wait a minute,' called Tom. 'I've never heard of anyone called Carl Neanderthal!'

'Well,' said Lila, 'maybe that's Lesson Number One—never lose your sense of humour!'

Answer on page 28

Lateral thinking
Each panel has something in common with the picture on either side. To make it harder for you, the answer is written back to front!

Fill in the missing pictures

If you managed to do the lateral thinking exercise on page 25, then you should have no trouble with this one. Again, each picture has something in common with its neighbour. Think about it and try to fill in the three missing pictures.

Answers on page 28

12   In Raptures

'What's so special about wrapping things?' wondered Tom. 'My mother wraps my lunch every day, does that make her an artist?'

'This is about wrapping big things,' explained Lila. 'You see, this fellow Christo has already wrapped the German Reichstag, and some cliffs in Sydney. The bigger the thing, the bigger the art. Now he's wrapped a whole city! Just look out the window. This exhibition here is just some of his earlier work.'

The parcels certainly looked very mysterious indeed, but was it art?

'When I'm grown up,' said Ben, 'I may wrap the whole planet Earth and be the biggest artist ever.'

Lila laughed. 'In the meantime,' she suggested, 'let's find out what these parcels here contain. They are all objects from somewhere in this very book. Ben, you take care of the yellow ones, Tom, you take the blue ones and I'll try to find out what the red ones are.'

Let me OUT!

CHRISTO junior
►RETROSPECTA◄

Beetlemania
Which of the beetles will be able to find their way out
and which will stay trapped forever?

You'll only get dizzy following the tracks with your eyes. Here's a tip: Count the lines. An even number means freedom, an odd number means the beetles stay trapped.

Solutions

1 Mouldy Maze

2 Flagging Faces

3 Domination

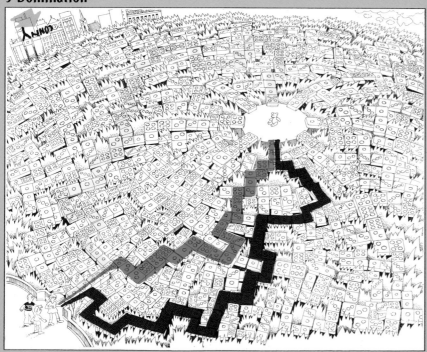

4 Paint the Tower Red!

Ben = red   Tom = blue   Lila = yellow

29

5 Problem Pets

6 Curly Christmas

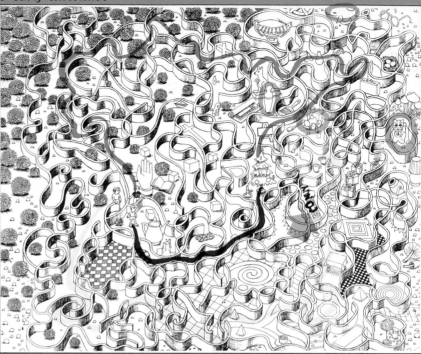

7 Alien Assignment

8 Chamber Chase

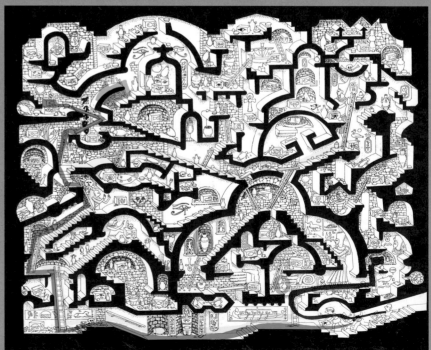

30

Ben = red   Tom = blue   Lila = yellow

9 Rubbish Retrieval

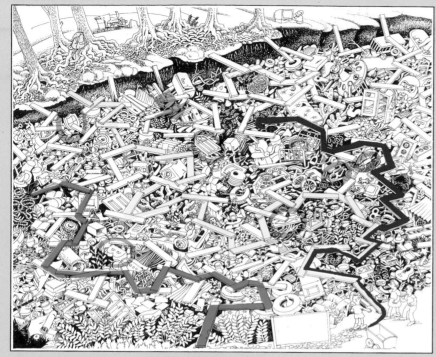

10 Bothersome Berries

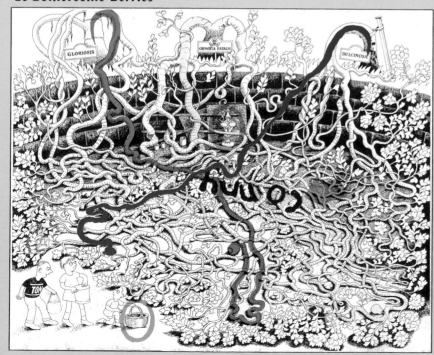

Ben = red   Tom = blue   Lila = yellow

11 Timeout

This is the path through in chronological order.

1 **Club.** Neanderthalers lived about 70,000 years ago, but their more primitive ancestors had already used such simple tools.
2 **Oar.** Oars found in Denmark have been dated to 7000BC.
3 **Wheel.** Wheels were used in Sumer in about 3500BC. Rollers had been used before.
4 **Writing.** In about 2200BC the Minoans used pen and ink for linear writing. Other methods had been used before.
5 **Compass.** Magnetic needles were probably used in China in 1115BC.
6 **Windmill.** About 700BC.
7 **Printing.** Gutenberg was the first European to use moveable type in about 1455.
8 **Microscope.** The Romans had already used glass balls filled with water as magnifying glasses, but in the 17th Century, Leeuwenhoek and others pioneered the building of proper microscopes.
9 **Balloon.** In 1783 the Montgolfier brothers staged the first manned hot air balloon flight.
10 **Steam Locomotive.** In 1804 Trevithick built the first self-propelled locomotive. (George Stephenson's railway opened in 1825.)
11 **Photography.** In 1826 Joseph Nicéphore Niépce made the first photograph. It took 8 hours to expose!
12 **Telegraph.** Invented in 1832 by Morse.
13 **Penny Farthing.** Invented by James Starley in 1871.
14 **Telephone.** Alexander Graham Bell patented the telephone in 1876.
15 **Electric Light.** Patented by Thomas Edison in 1879.
16 **Car.** 1885–first successful petrol-driven car by Karl-Friedrich Benz.
17 **X-rays.** Discovered in 1895 by Roentgen.
18 **Cinema.** In 1895 the Lumiére brothers made improvements on photographic equipment and patented the cinematograph.
19 **Radio.** Patented in 1896 by Marconi.
20 **Plane.** The Wright brothers made the first motorised flight in 1903.
21 **Television.** In 1924 John Logie Baird transmitted the first television pictures.
22 **Satellites.** The first man-made satellite was the Sputnik, sent into orbit by the Russians in 1957.
23 **Moon Walk.** In 1969 Neil Armstrong and Edwin Aldrin were the first men to walk on the moon.
24 **Personal Computers.** Having been improved over a number of decades, computers came into wider use in the 1970s.

12 In Raptures

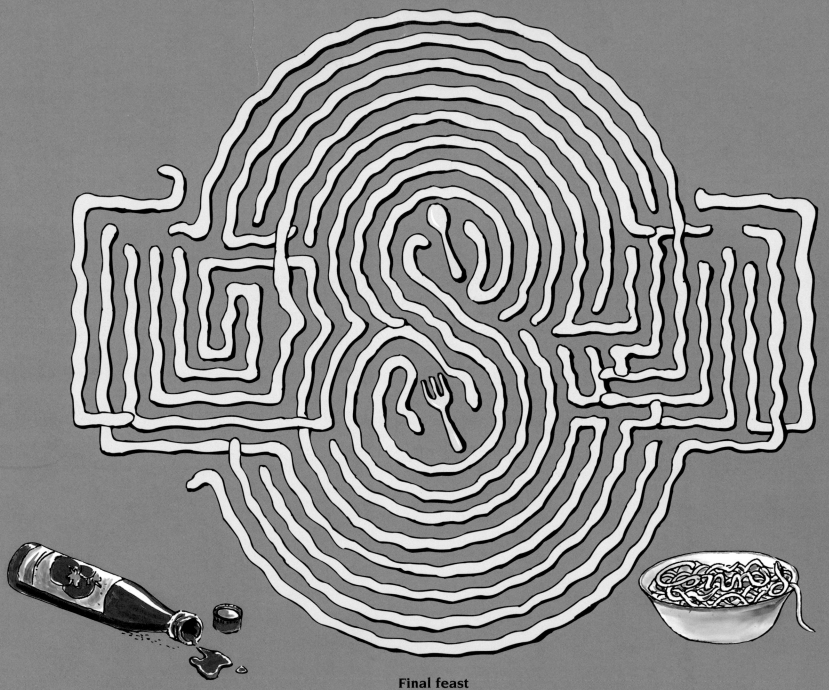

Final feast
Here's a last maze to whet your appetite for more of
Rolf Heimann's amazing mazes. If you don't want to eat the
spaghetti with your fingers, get yourself a fork and spoon.